TODAY'S CH
HITS

Published by

WISE PUBLICATIONS
14-15 Berners Street, London W1T 3LJ, UK

Exclusive Distributors:

MUSIC SALES LIMITED
Distribution Centre, Newmarket Road,
Bury St Edmunds, Suffolk IP33 3YB, UK

MUSIC SALES PTY LIMITED
20 Resolution Drive,
Caringbah, NSW 2229, Australia

Order No. AM1002177
ISBN 978-1-84938-817-7

Edited by Jenni Wheeler.
Cover designed by Lizzie Barrand.

Printed in the EU

www.musicsales.com

TODAY'S CHART
HITS

WISE PUBLICATIONS
PART OF THE MUSIC SALES GROUP
LONDON / NEW YORK / PARIS / SYDNEY / COPENHAGEN / BERLIN / MADRID / HONG KONG / TOKYO

Owl City

Fireflies

Words & Music by Adam Young

lit up the world as I fell a - sleep.
as they tried to teach me how to dance;
'Cause they'd fill the o - pen air
a fox trot a - bove my head,
and leave tear - drops ev - 'ry - where. You'd think me rude but I would just stand and
a sock hop be - neath my bed, a dis - co ball that's just hang - ing by a
1.
A♭
E♭/G
B♭sus4
4fr
3fr
stare.
thread.
I'd like to make my - self be - lieve that pla - net earth
A♭
E♭
Gm
A♭
E♭
4fr
6fr
3fr
4fr
6fr
turns slow - ly. It's hard to say that I'd rath - er stay a -

A♭
B♭
Cm
A♭
E♭
F
-wake when I'm a-sleep. 'Cause ev-'ry-thing is nev-er as it seems.
2.
A♭
Cm
B♭
A♭
E♭
I'd like to make my-self be-lieve that pla-net earth turns
Gm
A♭
E♭
A♭
B♭
Cm
slow - ly. It's hard to say that I'd rath-er stay a-wake when I'm a-sleep. 'Cause

A♭
4fr
E♭
6fr
B♭
N.C.
ev-'ry-thing is nev-er as it seems when I fall a-sleep.
B♭
E♭
6fr
A♭
4fr
Leave my door o-pen just a crack (Please take me a-way from
B♭
E♭
6fr
A♭
4fr
here.) 'cause I feel like such an in-som - ni-ac. (Please take me a-way from
B♭
E♭
6fr
A♭
4fr
here.) Why do I tire of count-ing sheep (Please take me a-way from

B♭
E♭
6fr
A♭
4fr
N.C.
here.) when I'm far too ti - red to fall a - sleep?
To ten mil - lion fire - flies I'm weird 'cause I hate good - byes.
I got mist - y eyes as they said fare - well.
But I'll know where sev - 'ral are if my dreams get real bi - zarre, 'cause I

B♭
E♭
A♭
N.C.
6fr
4fr
3fr
saved a few and I keep them in a jar.
A♭
Cm
B♭
E♭
I'd like to make my-self be-lieve that pla-net earth turns
Gm
slow - ly. It's hard to say that I'd rath-er stay a - wake when I'm a - sleep. 'Cause
F
E♭/G
ev - 'ry - thing is nev - er as it seems when I fall a -

A♭
Cm
B♭
-sleep. I'd like to make my-self be-lieve that pla-net Earth
E♭
Gm
turns slow - - ly. It's
hard to say that I'd rath-er stay a-wake when I'm a-sleep. 'Cause
ev-'ry-thing is nev-er as it seems when I fall a-
4fr
3fr
6fr

A♭
Cm
B♭
4fr
3fr
-sleep. I'd like to make my-self be-lieve that pla-net Earth
A♭
E♭
Gm
A♭
E♭
6fr
turns slow-ly. It's hard to say that I'd rath-er stay a-
A♭
B♭
Cm
A♭
E♭
B♭
-wake when I'm a-sleep. Be-cause my dreams are burst-ing at the seams.
B♭sus4
B♭
3

The Script

For The First Time

Words & Music by Mark Sheehan & Daniel O'Donoghue

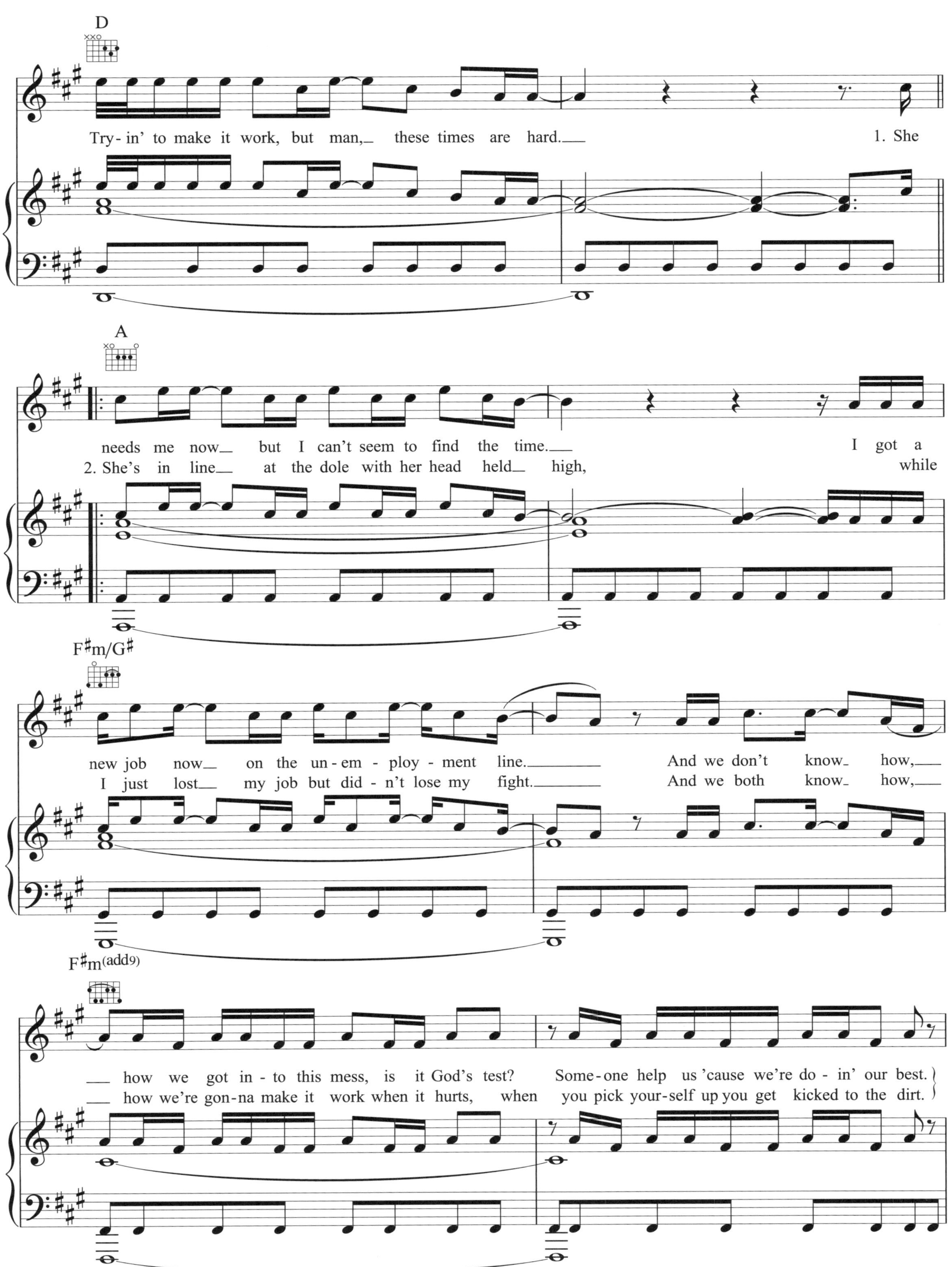
D
Try- in' to make it work, but man, these times are hard. 1. She
A
needs me now but I can't seem to find the time. I got a
2. She's in line at the dole with her head held high, while
F#m/G#
new job now on the un - em - ploy - ment line. And we don't know how,
I just lost my job but did - n't lose my fight. And we both know how,
F#m(add9)
how we got in - to this mess, is it God's test? Some-one help us 'cause we're do - in' our best.
how we're gon-na make it work when it hurts, when you pick your-self up you get kicked to the dirt.

D
Try-in' to make it work, but man,_ these times are hard._ But we're gon-na start_ by
F♯m7
drink-ing old cheap bot-tles of wine,_
Dadd9
2fr
sit talk-in' up_ all night._
A
Say-in' things we have-n't for_ a while._
2° Do-in'
F♯m/G♯
A while,_ yeah._ We're
F♯m7
smil-ing but we're close to tears._
Dadd9
2fr
E-ven af-ter all_ these years,_ we just_

A
Esus4
now got the feel - ing that we're meet - ing for the first time.
A
A/G♯
Ooh.
Ooh.
F♯m7
Ooh.
Dmaj7
1.
2.

F♯m7
Dadd9
2fr
Drink - ing old cheap bot - tles of wine,
sit talk - in' up all night.
A
E
Say - in' things we have - n't for a while.
We're
F♯m7
Dadd9
2fr
smil - ing but we're close to tears.
E - ven af - ter all these years, we just
A
E5
now got the feel - ing that we're meet - ing for the first time.

A
A/G♯
Ooh.
Ooh.
F♯m7
Ooh.
Dmaj7
A
Just now got the feel - ing that we're meet - ing for the first time. Oh, these times are hard
A/G♯
Yeah, they're mak-ing us cra - zy. Don't give up on me ba - by.

F♯m7
Dmaj7
Oh, these times are hard. Yeah, they're mak-ing us cra - zy. Don't give up on me ba-
A
- by.
Oh, these times are hard Yeah, they're mak-ing us cra-
A/G♯
F♯m7
- zy. Don't give up on me ba - by.
Oh, these times are hard.
Dmaj7
E7sus4
rit.
A
Yeah, they're mak-ing us cra - zy. Don't give up on me ba - by.

Bruno Mars

Just The Way You Are (Amazing)

Words & Music by Peter Hernandez, Philip Lawrence,
Ari Levine, Khari Cain & Khalil Walton

B♭
perfectly without her trying. She's so beautiful
F
and I tell her ev'ry day.
Yeah,
I know, I know when I compliment her she won't believe me.
Dm
And it's so, it's so sad to think that she don't see what I see.

B♭
But ev-'ry time she asks me "Do I look o-kay?" I say:
F
When I see your face,
F
Dm
there's not a thing that I would change 'cause you're a-maz-
B♭
-ing just the way you are.
F

And when you smile, the whole world stops
Dm
and stares for a while. 'Cause girl you're a - maz - ing
B♭
just
the way you are.
F
Yeah.
2. Her lips, her lips I could kiss them all day if she'd let me.

Dm
Her laugh, her laugh, she hates, but I think it's so sex - y.
B♭
She's so beau - ti - ful and I tell her ev - 'ry
F
day.
Oh you know, you know, you know I'd nev - er
ask you to change.
Dm
If per-fect's what you're search-ing for then just stay the same.
So

B♭
don't e - ven both - er ask - ing if you look o - kay, you know I'll
F
say:
F
When I see your face,
Dm
there's not a thing that I would change 'cause you're a - maz-
B♭
- ing just the way you are.
F

And when you smile, the whole world stops
Dm
and stares for a while. 'Cause girl, you're a - maz - ing
B♭
just
the way you are.
F
The way you are,
the way you are,
Dm

B♭
girl, you're a - maz - ing just the way you are.
F
When I see your face,
Dm
there's not a thing that I would change
B♭
'cause you're a - maz - ing just

F
the way you are.
And when you smile,
Dm
the whole world stops and stares for a while.
B♭
'Cause girl, you're a - maz - ing
just
F
the way you are.
Yeah.

Enrique Iglesias feat. Pitbull

I Like It

Words & Music by Nadir Khayat, Enrique Iglesias,
Lionel Richie & Armando Perez

F
Am
G
Go, go, go D. J. Go, go, go D. J. Club is on fire. 1. Oh,
F 2nd inv.
A – 2nd inv.
G – 2nd inv.
G
F
Am
girl, please ex-cuse me if I'm com-in' to you strong, but to-night is the night we can
(2.) girl, please ex-cuse me if I'm mis-be-hav-in', oh. I'm try'n' to keep my hands off, but you're
G 1st in
Am 1st inv.
G
F
real-ly let go. My girl-friend's out-ta town and I'm all a-lone. Your
beg-ging me for more. Round, round, round give a low, low, low. Let the
Am
G
boy-friend's on va-ca-tion and he does-n't have to know. No. Oh, oh, oh.
time, time, pass 'cause we're nev-er get-tin' old. No. Oh, oh, oh.

F
Am
G
No - one can do the things I'm gon - na wan - na do to you. No.
No - one can do it bet - ter, turn a - round I'll give you more. No.
F
Am
Oh, oh.
Oh, oh.
Oh, shout a - loud, scream a - loud,
G
N.C.
G
F
let me hear you go. Ba - by, I like it, the way you move on the floor. Ba - by, I
Am
G
like it. Come on and give me some more. Oh, yes I like it. Scream - ing like

F
Am
G
1.
never before. Baby, I like it. I, I, I like it.
Party, karamu,
fi - es - ta, for - ev - er.
2. Oh,
2.
Come D. J. That's my D. J.
I'm a Mi-am - i boy, you know how we play.
I ain't play-in' with you but I wan-na play with you. Give me, got me good. Now watch me.

F
It's a diff-'rent spe-cies. Look at me in D. C. let's par-ty on the White House lawn.
Am
G
Ti-ger Woods times Jes-se James_ e-quals Pit-bull all night long. Pick up Ba-
F
-rack and Mi-chelle, let 'em know that it's on. Pa' fue-ra! Pa' la cal-le!
Am
G
Da-le ma-mi-ta ti-ra-me e-se bai-le! Da-le ma-mi-ta ti-ra-me e-se bai-le!

F
Am
I see you watch-in' me,
you see me watch-in' you.
I love the way you move,
G
N.C.
G
F
I like them things you do, like. Don't stop ba-by, don't stop ba-by.
Am
G
Just keep on shak-ing a-long.
I
F
Am
won't stop ba-by, won't stop ba-by, un-til you get e-nough.

G
Par - ty, ka - ra - mu,
F
Am
G
fi - es - ta, for - ev - er.
Ba - by, I
G
F
Am
like it, the way you move on the floor. Ba - by, I like it. Come on and
G
F
give me some more. Oh, yes I like it. Scream - ing like nev - er be - fore. Ba - by, I

1.
2.
Am
G
like it. I, I, I like it. Ba - by, I like it.
G
F
Oh, yes I like it.
Vocal ad lib.
Am
G
Oh, yes I like it.
F
Am
G
Repeat to fade
Oh, yes I like it.

Brandon Flowers

Only The Young

Words & Music by Brandon Flowers

F
C/E
Dm7
Where did the bow break?
It hap-pened be - fore your time.
And there were peo -
F
C
C/B
- ple there, love - ly as you've ev - er cared.
To - night.
Am
G
F
Ba - by you can start a - gain, laughing in the o - pen air, have your-self an - oth -
C
C/B
Am
G
- er dream.
To-night.
Ba - by, we can start a - gain.

F
C
C/B
Am
G
On - ly the young can break a-way, break a-way. Lost when the wind blows, on your own, oh.
F
C
C/B
Am
G
On - ly the young can break a-way, break a-way. Lost when the wind blows, on your own, oh.
F
C
Cadd9/B
Am
G
To Coda
F
C
Cadd9/B
Am
G

F
C/E
F
C/E
E
2. Moth-er it's cold__ here.
Fa-ther, thy will__ be______ done.__
F
C
Em
Am
Thun-der and light - ning are crash-ing down. They got me on the
G
E
F
C
C/B
run, di-rect me to the sun. Re-demp-tion keeps_ my cov-ers clean.___ To-night._
Am
G
D.S. al Coda
__ Ba - by, we__ can start a - gain.______

Coda
Am
G
C
F
Am
G
C
F
And the sun will shine a - gain.
And the sun will shine a - gain.
Dm
Em
Am
G
Dm
F
Are you look - ing for the sign?
Or are you caught up in the love light?
F
C
Cadd9/B
Am
G
(Ha, ha, ha, ha, ha.)
F
C
Cadd9/B
Am
G
(Ha, ha, ha, ha, ha.)

F
C
C/B
Am
G
On - ly the young can break a-way, break a-way. Lost when the wind blows, on your own, oh.
F
C
C/B
Am
G
On - ly the young can break a-way, break a-way. Lost when the wind blows, on your own, oh.
F
C
Em7
Am
G
On - ly the young can... Lost when the wind blows.
F
C
Em7
Am
G
On - ly the young can... (Ha, ha, ha, ha.) Lost when the wind blows.

I Am Kloot

Proof

Words & Music by John Bramwell, Andrew Hargreaves
& Peter Jobson

E
B/D♯
Say, d'you wan-na spin an-oth-er line, like we had a good
C♯m
4fr
B
E
time, not that I need proof. Swell, we're liv-ing in a ho-
B/D♯
C♯m
4fr
-tel and some-one's ring-ing my bell in a room with-out a view.
B
E
Hey, heard you read an-oth-er

B/D♯
C♯m
4fr
Pause 1° only
book. Should I take an-oth - er look? Who am I with-out
E
B/D♯
C♯m
4fr
you?
A - hoo,
B
E
ah,
a - hoo.
B/D♯
C♯m
4fr
B
Ah,
ah.

E
B/D♯
La-la - la-la - la-la - la-la - la-la - la-la - la-la - la-la - la-la.

1.
C♯m
4fr
B
La-la - la-la - la-la - la-la - la-la - la-la - la-la - la-la - la-la.

2.
C♯m
4fr
B
La-la - la-la - la-la - la-la - la-la - la-la - la-la - la-la - la-la - la-la - la-la.

Kings Of Leon

Sex On Fire

Words & Music by Caleb Followill, Nathan Followill, Jared Followill & Matthew Followill

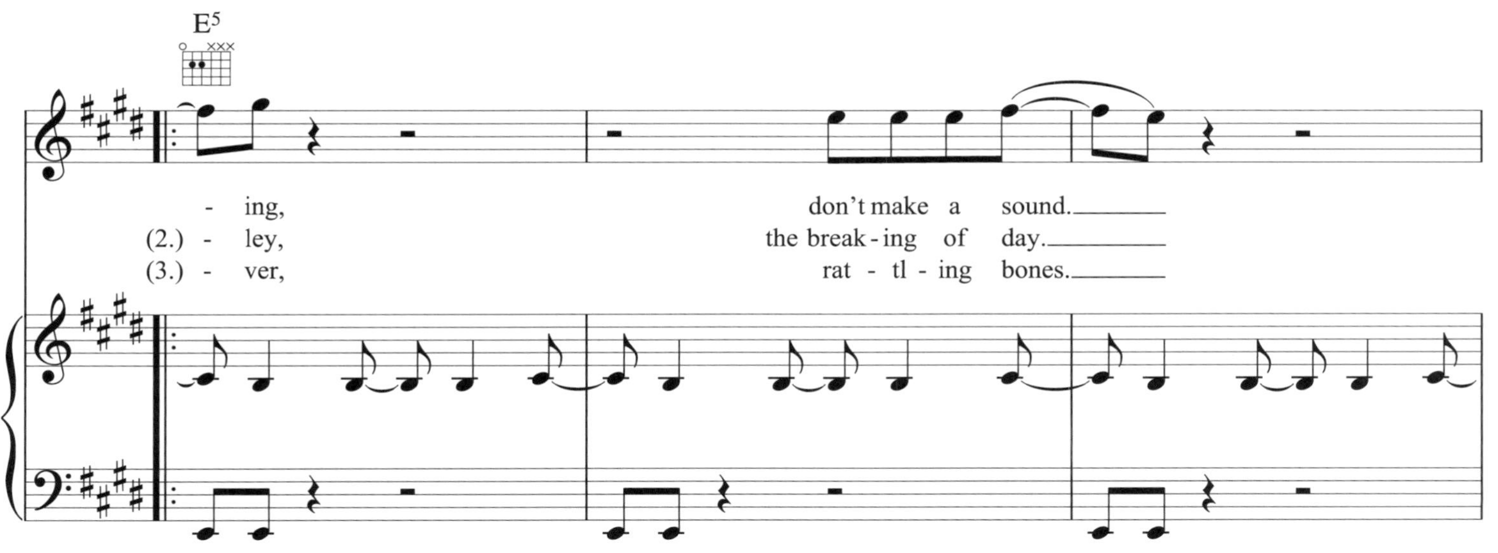
E5
- ing,
don't make a sound.
(2.) - ley,
the break - ing of day.
(3.) - ver,
rat - tl - ing bones.

C#m
I know they're watch - ing,
they're watch -
The head while I'm driv - ing,
I'm driv -
I can just taste it,
taste

E
- ing.
All the com - mo - tion,
- ing.
Soft lips are o - pen,
it.
If it's not for - ev - er,

the kid - die like play,
the knuck-les are pale,
if it's just to - night,
it has peo - ple talk -
feels like you're dy -
oh, it's still the great -

C#m
4fr
- ing,
- ing,
- est,
they're talk - ing.
you're dy - ing.
the great - est, the great - est.

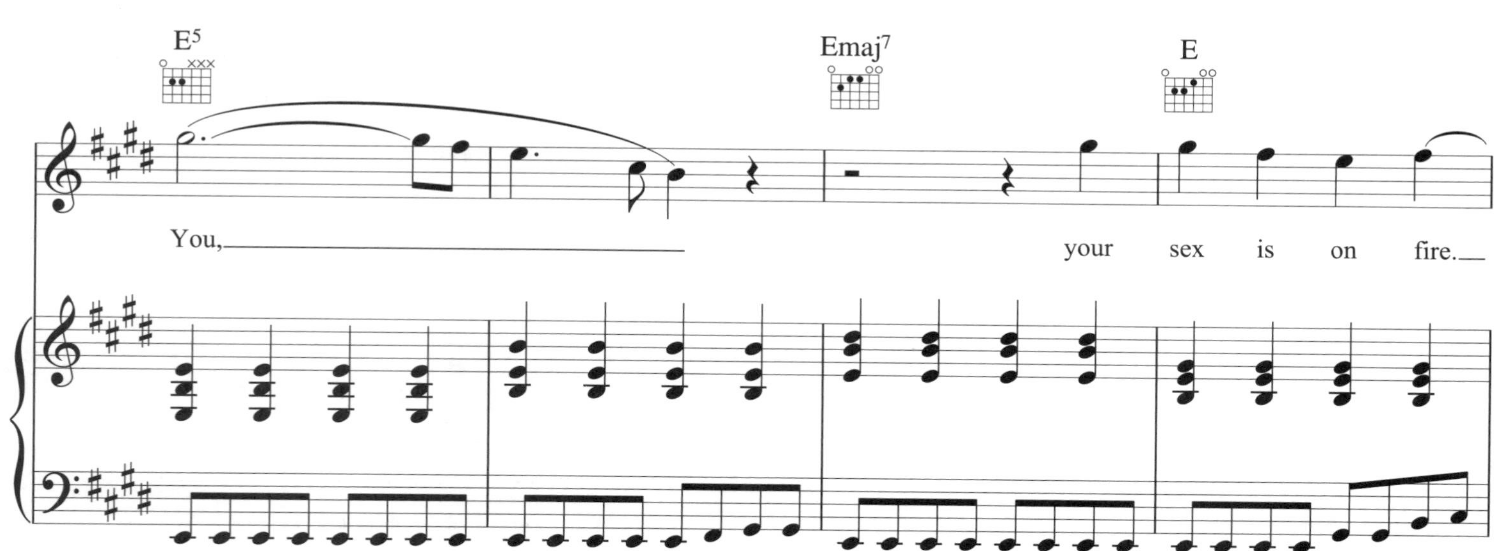
E5
Emaj7
E
You,
your sex is on fire.

C♯m7
4fr
Amaj9
To Coda ⊕
1.
2. The dark of the al -
E5
Con - sumed
Emaj7
E
C♯m7
4fr
with what's to trans - pire.
Amaj9
D.S. al Coda
3. Hot as a fe -

Coda
Amaj9
E
You,
your
C♯m7
4fr
sex is on fire.
Ah.
E5
Emaj7
Con - sumed
with
E
C♯m7
4fr
Amaj9
what's to trans - pire.

E5
Emaj7
E
You, your sex is on fire.
C#m7
4fr
Amaj9
Con-sumed
E5
Emaj7
E
with what's to trans - pire.
C#m7
4fr
Amaj9
E

Robbie Williams & Gary Barlow

Shame

Words & Music by Robbie Williams & Gary Barlow

B♭ Cm7 B♭/D E♭ B♭/D C7
3fr 6fr
And we can put it down to cir-cum-stance, our child-hood then our youth.
♩ = ♩ F7 Gm
3fr
Out of some sen-ti-men-tal gain I want-ed you to feel my pain,
E♭ B♭ Cm7 B♭/D
6fr 3fr
but it came back re-turn to send-er.
F7 Gm
3fr
I read your mind and tried to call, my tears could fill the Al-bert Hall.

E♭
6fr
F
Is this the sound of sweet sur-ren - der?
What a shame we
B♭
Cm7
3fr
E♭
6fr
F
B♭
Cm7
3fr
nev - er list - ened.
I told you through the tel - e - vi - sion.
E♭
6fr
F
B♭
Cm7
3fr
E♭
6fr
F
And all that went a - way was the price we paid.
Peo-ple spend a
Gm
3fr
C
F7
life - time this way.
Oh what a shame.

B♭
Cm7
B♭/D
E♭
B♭/D
Cm7
2. So I got bu-sy throw-ing ev-'ry-bod-y un-der-neath the bus. Oh.
B♭
Cm7
B♭/D
E♭
B♭/D
C7
And with your post-er thir-ty foot high at the back of Toys 'R' Us.
F7
Gm
I wrote a let-ter in my mind, but the words were so un-kind,
E♭
B♭
Cm7
B♭/D
a-bout a man I can't re-mem-ber.

F7
Gm
3fr
I don't re - call the rea - sons why, I must have meant them at the time.
Eb
6fr
F
Is this the sound of sweet sur-ren - der?
What a shame we
Bb
Cm7
3fr
Eb
6fr
F
Bb
Cm7
3fr
nev - er list - ened.
I told you through the tel - e - vi - sion.
Eb
6fr
F
Bb
Cm7
3fr
Eb
6fr
F
And all that went a - way was the price we paid.
Peo-ple spend a

Gm
C
Gm
3fr
life - time this way.
And that's how they stay.
C
F
B♭
G7
C
Oh what a shame.
Words come eas - y
Cm
F7
B♭
B♭
G7
C
Cm
F(sus2/4)
B♭
when they're true.
Words come eas - y when they're true.
B♭
Cm
E♭
F
6fr
So I got bus - y throw - ing ev - 'ry - bod - y un - der - neath the bus.

B♭
Cm
3fr
E♭
6fr
F
B♭
Cm
3fr
And with your post - er thir - ty foot high at the back of Toys 'R' Us. Now we can put it down to
E♭
6fr
F
cir - cum - stance, our child - hood then our youth.
What a shame we
B♭
Cm7
3fr
E♭
6fr
F
B♭
Cm7
3fr
nev - er list - ened.
I told you through the tel - e - vi - sion.
E♭
6fr
F
B♭
Cm7
3fr
E♭
6fr
F
And all that went a - way was the price we paid.
Peo - ple spend a

Gm
3fr
C
Gm
3fr
life - time this way.
And that's how they stay.
C
Gm
3fr
C
Peo-ple spend a life - time this way.
Oh what a shame,
F7
B♭
Cm7
3fr
B♭/D
what a shame.
E♭
6fr
B♭/D
C7
Cm7
3fr
B♭
Ooh.
Such a shame, what a shame.

Plan B

She Said

Words & Music by Benjamin Ballance-Drew,
Eric Appapoulay, Richard Cassell & Tom Goss

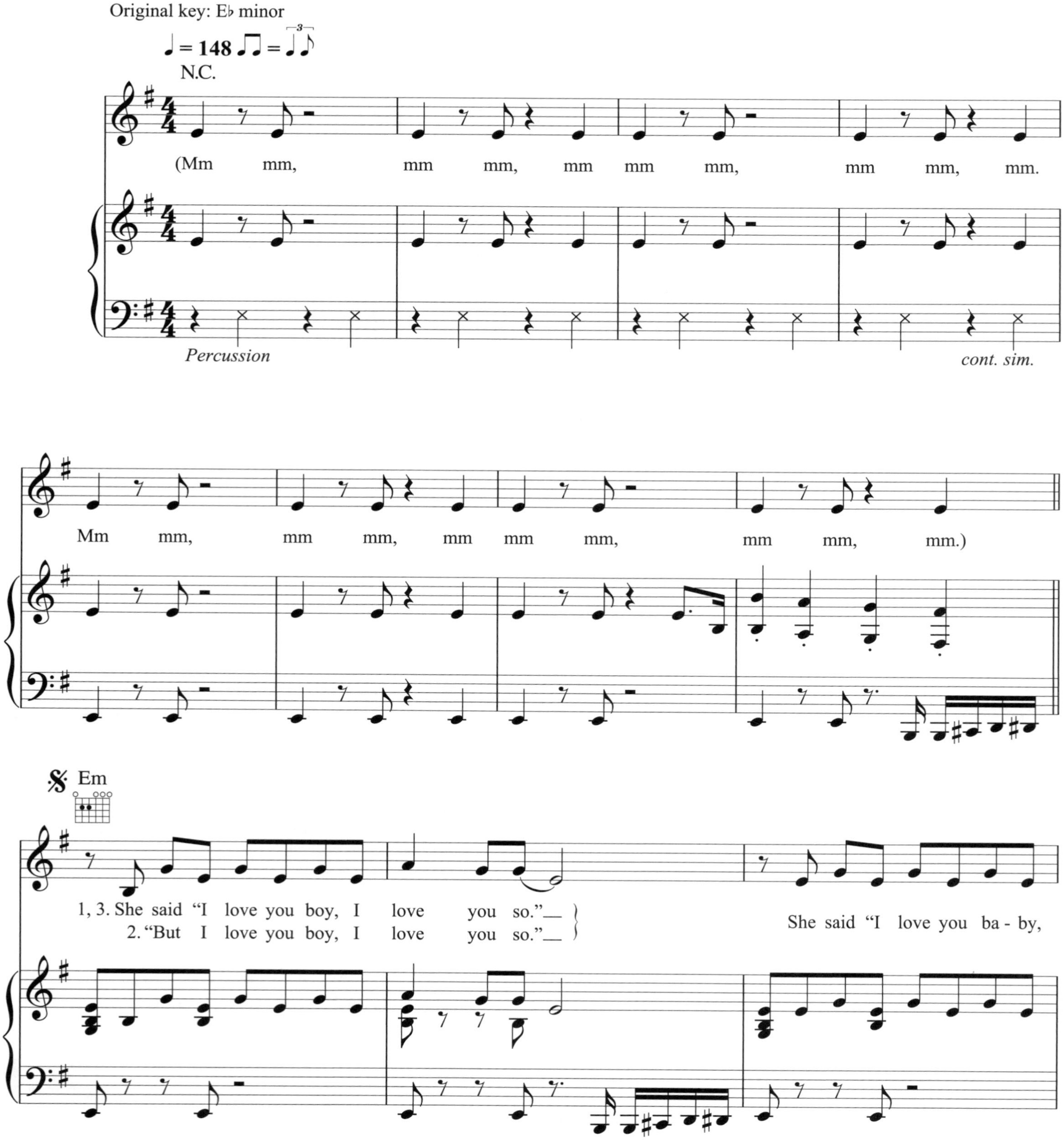

Mm mm, mm mm, mm mm mm, mm mm, mm.)

𝄋 Em

1, 3. She said "I love you boy, I love you so."
2. "But I love you boy, I love you so."

She said "I love you ba - by,

B7
oh, oh, oh, oh, oh."
Em
She said "I love you more than words can say."
B7
To Coda II
She said "I love you ba - a - a - a - a - by."
To Coda I

Em
Drums
Em
So I said
"What you're say - ing girl, it
can't be right.
B7
How can you be in love with me?
We on - ly just met to - night."
Em
So she said

B7
G
"Boy, I loved you from the start.
When I first heard 'Love Goes Down'
something started burning
in my heart."
I said "Stop this cra - zy
talk,
and leave right

B
D.S. al Coda I
now and close the door."
She said
Coda I
Em
So now I'm up in the courts, plead-ing my case from the wit - ness box.
'Cause she like the sound of my mu - sic, which makes her a fan of my mu - sic.
Tell - ing the judge and the jur - y the same thing that I said to the cops
'S'why 'Love Goes Down' makes her lose it, 'cause she can't sep-a-rate the man from the mu - sic.
B
on the day that I got ar - rest - ed "I'm in - no- cent" I pro - test - ed.
And I'm say - ing all this in the stand while my girl cries tears in the gal - ler - y.

1.
She just feels re - ject - ed, had her heart bro-ken by some-one she's ob-sessed with.
This has got big-ger than I ev - er could have planned,
2.
G
like that song by the Zu-tons, 'Val-er-ie'.
'Cept the jur-y don't look like they're buy-ing it,
B
this is mak-ing me ner-vous.
Arms crossed, screwed face, like I'm try-ing it,
G
their eyes fixed on me like I'm mur-der-ous.
They wan-na lock me up

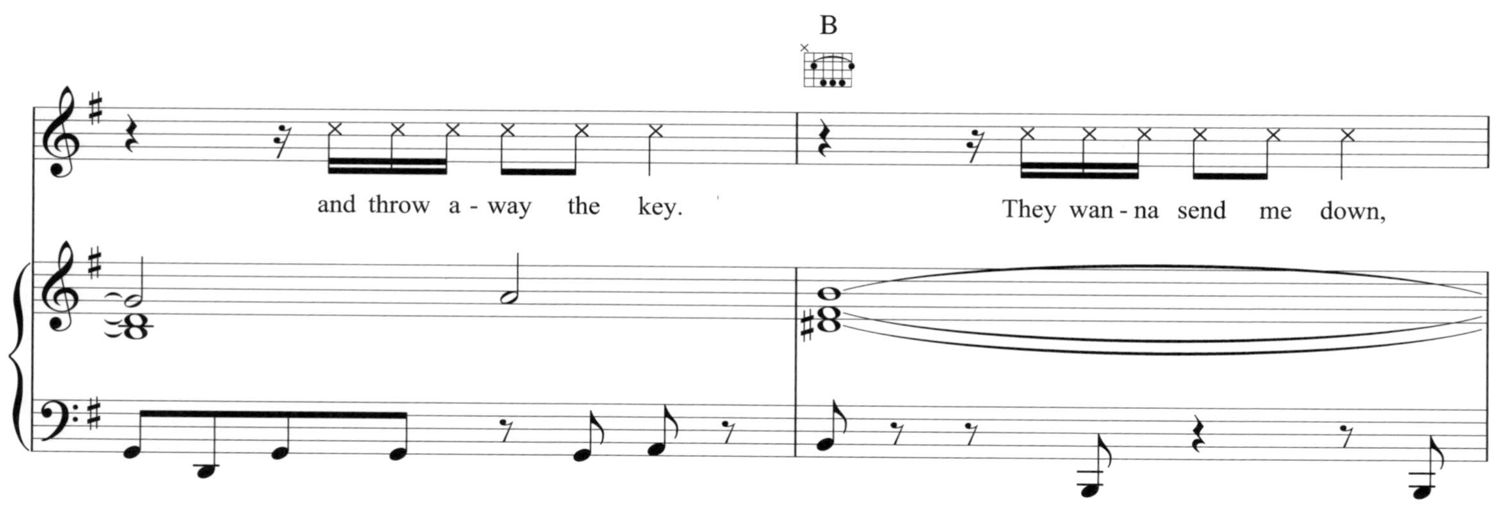
B
and throw a-way the key.
They wan-na send me down,

B7
N.C.
e-ven though I told them she...
Drums

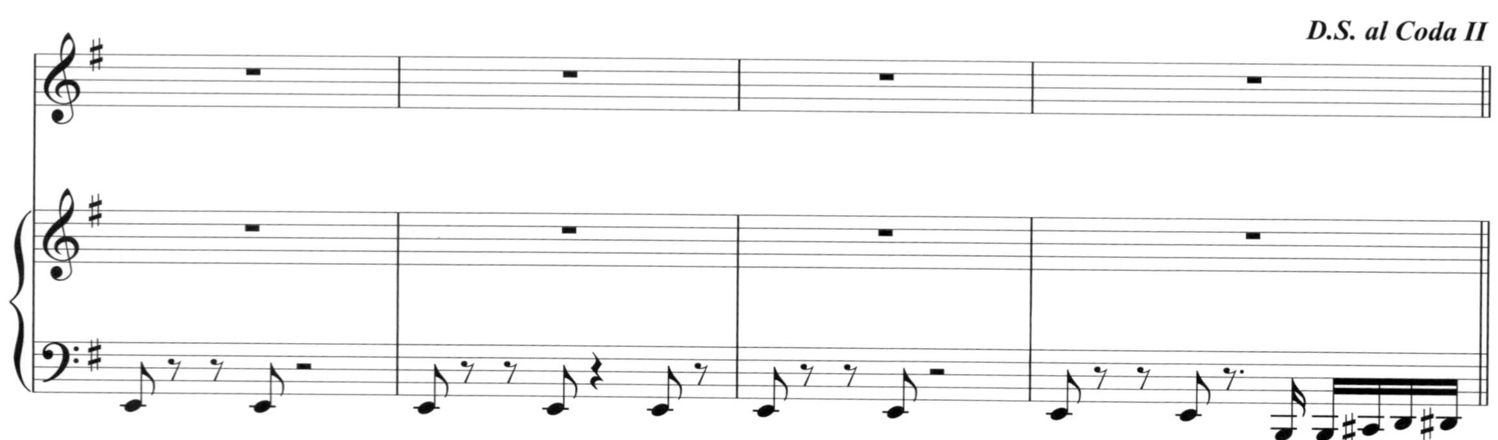
D.S. al Coda II

Coda II
B7
So I said "Then why the hell you got-ta treat me this way?
Em
You don't know what love is.
You
B7
3
would-n't do this if you did."
rit.
N.C.
Esus4
No no no no.
Oh.

Coldplay

Viva La Vida

Words & Music by Guy Berryman, Jon Buckland,
Will Champion & Chris Martin

D♭maj7
4fr
E♭7
6fr
A♭
4fr
Fm
sleep a - lone, sweep the streets I used to own.
D♭
4fr
E♭7
6fr
A♭
4fr
Fmadd9
D♭
4fr
E♭7
6fr
A♭
4fr
Fmadd9
2. I used to
D♭maj7
4fr
E♭7
6fr
A♭
4fr
roll the dice, feel the fear in my en - e - my's eyes.
(3.) wild wind, blew down the doors to let me in.

Fm
D♭maj7
E♭7
Listened as the crowd would sing, "Now the
Shattered windows and the sound of drums. People
A♭
Fm
D♭
E♭7
old king is dead, long live the king." One minute I held the key, next the
couldn't believe what I'd become. Revolutionaries wait for my
A♭
Fm
D♭maj7
walls were closed on me and I discovered that my castles stand
head on a silver plate. Just a puppet on a lonely string.
E♭7
A♭
Fm
upon pillars of salt and pillars of sand.
Oh, who would ever wanna be king?
I
4fr
6fr

D♭maj7
4fr
E♭7
6fr
A♭
4fr
Fm9
6fr
hear Je - ru - sa - lem bells a - ring - ing. Ro - man Cav - al - ry choirs are sing - ing.
D♭maj7
4fr
E♭7
6fr
A♭
4fr
Fm9
6fr
Be my mir - ror, my sword and shield. My mis - sion - ar - ies in a for - eign field.
D♭maj7
4fr
E♭
6fr
A♭/C
For some rea - son I can't ex - plain,
once you'd gone there was
I know Saint Pe - ter won't call
Fm11
D♭maj7
4fr
E♭7
6fr
nev - er, nev - er an hon - est word, and that was
my name. Nev - er an hon - est word, but that was

A♭maj9
3fr
Fm7
To Coda I
To Coda II
D♭
4fr
when I ruled the world.
when I ruled the world.
E♭7
6fr
A♭
4fr
1.
Fm7
2.
Fm7
D.S. al Coda I
3. It was the wick-ed and
Coda I
D♭
4fr
Fm
D♭
4fr
Fm
D♭
4fr
Fm
E♭7
6fr

D♭maj7
4fr
E♭7
6fr
Oh.
Oh.
A♭
4fr
Fm11
D♭maj7
4fr
Oh.
E♭7
6fr
A♭
4fr
Fm11
D.S.S. al Coda II
Oh.
Oh.
Coda II
D♭maj7
4fr
E♭7
6fr
A♭maj9
3fr
Fm
Repeat and fade
Ooh.

Jason Derülo

What If

Words & Music by Jason Desrouleaux & Jonathan Rotem

Am
Em7
F
C
This is the first I've seen your face, but there's a chance we are soul - mates. I
It could hap - pen, raise three kids and we'd grow old, oh, so hap - pi - ly. I
F
C
Em
know this might sound cra - zy 'cause you don't know my name.
know this might sound cra - zy 'cause I don't know your name.
F
C
G
Am
F
Am7
But we can't, we can't tell the fu - ture, no. But that's just the beau - ty
G
F
C
G
Am
of the world we know. So I'm - a say do - do, do - do, do - do, do - do. Ba - by, what if?

1.
F
Am7
G
Am
Em
We all can say do-do, do-do, do-do, do-do. Ba-by, what if? (What if?) What if?
F
C
F
C
Em
(What if?) What if? (What if?) What if? Yeah.
2.
F
Em
F
Don't know what to-mor-row brings but I'm still hop-ing that you are the one for me.
Am
G/B
F
G
Oh, and what if I had you and what if you had me and ba-by, what's

E/G♯
2fr
Am
Em
the rea - son we can't fall in love?
What if?
F
C
F
C
Em
(What if?) What if? (What if?) What if? Oh!
F
C
G
Am
F
Am7
But we can't, we can't tell the fu - ture, no. But that's just the beau - ty
G
F
C
G
Am
of the world we know. So I'm - a say do - do, do - do, do - do, do - do. Ba - by, what if?

F
Am7
G
We all can say do - do, do - do, do - do, do - do. Ba - by, what if?
F
C
G
Am
F
Am7
But we can't, we can't tell the fu - ture, no. But that's just the beau - ty
G
F
C
G
Am
of the world we know. So I'm - a say do - do, do - do, do - do, do - do. Ba - by, what if?
F
Am7
G
N.C.
We all can say do - do, do - do, do - do, do - do. Ba - by, what if?

1 2 3 4 5 6 7 8 9